TEREZÍN
SMALL FORTRESS
1940-1945

A Guide to the
Permanent Exhibition in Terezín
Small Fortress Museum

PERMANENT EXHIBITION "TEREZÍN SMALL FORTRESS 1940-1945"

Small Fortress Museum building.

Late 1950s permanent exhibition.

The former Small Officers' Pavilion within the Small Fortress was completed in 1784. It served as a military accommodation facility throughout the existence of the Habsburg monarchy as well as in the times of the First Czechoslovak Republic. When the German occupying power decided to convert the Terezín Small Fortress to a Gestapo prison in 1940, the structure became a barracks again, this time to house an SS guard unit.

The end of the war was not to be the end of the building's turbulent history, not to mention that of the Small Fortress as a whole. An auxiliary hospital of the Czech Action for Help (ČPA) was stationed inside it temporarily in May 1945. Between the summer of 1945 and early 1948, it housed a National Security Corps (SNB) unit on duty in an detention camp for Germans.

Today the building houses the permanent exhibition "Terezín Small Fortress 1940-1945": the seventh permanent museum exhibition to occupy the premises, which have hardly changed structurally. The first permanent exhibition opened as early as 1949. That was preceded by a Czecho-

Late 1960s permanent exhibition.

One of the Small Fortress Museum rooms after the August 2002 flood.

*The same exhibition room
after the 2003 reinstallation.*

slovak Government Resolution of May 6, 1947, establishing a Memorial to National Suffering in the Small Fortress, renamed the Terezín Memorial in 1964. The first permanent exhibition as well as those that followed were largely affected by the ruling ideology of the time.

It was only the democratic change after November 1989 that made it possible to present the history of the Terezín Gestapo prison in an objective way. Partial modifications were made to the existing permanent exhibition at first, removing and correcting the major misinterpretations of the historic events. A brand new exhibition opened in 1994: the first one to introduce the visitors to the stories of all the groups of prisoners as well as the broader context of the Nazi occupation policy implemented in the Czech Lands in 1939-1945.

The exhibition explains the events after the ascent of Nazism to power until the breaking of the then Czechoslovakia, the occupation of the Czech Lands, and the nature and principal directions of the Czech resistance movement. The further sections then deal with the history of the Gestapo prison in the Small Fortress and the stories of its inmates.

Along with the other buildings and grounds of the Terezín Memorial, the permanent exhibition suffered severe damage due to the disastrous flood of 2002. Thanks to extensive assistance granted by the Ministry of Culture of the Czech Republic and donations by friends abroad, it was able to reopen after reinstallation and additions only a year later.

The exhibition reflects the status quo of the research carried out by the Terezín Memorial in cooperation with other institutions and individual scholars.

THE EXPANSION OF NAZI GERMANY AND CZECHOSLOVAKIA

The Czechoslovak Republic was established in the autumn of 1918 alongside other countries in the territory of the pre-existent Austria-Hungary, which belonged to the defeated powers of World War One. Within inter-war Europe, it was one of the few truly democratic countries with constitutions based on huma-nist principles. From its very beginning, it had to face the efforts of those who would not come to terms with the new situation in Europe, characterised by the emergence of numerous national states, and who worked towards its revision. Those efforts became much stronger after the Nazi ascent to power in Germany.

The appointment of Adolf Hitler as the Chancellor of the German Reich on January 30, 1933, posed a mortal danger to Czechoslovakia. Hitler regarded the country as an obstruction on his way to the shattering of the after-war European system and the attainment of a dominant position of Germany on the European continent. The issue of the German minority, concentrated chiefly in the Czech borderlands, became a suitable pretext for his gradual undermining of the international position of the Czechoslovak Republic and its eventual total destruction. The minority problem was made more tense and gradually internationalised by means of demagogic propaganda. Its dissemination found breeding ground in the economic and social repercussions of the global economic crisis of the early 1930s, which badly affected the Czechoslovak borderlands with a high proportion of light export industry. The German National Socialist Workers' Party (DNSAP) and the German National Party (DNP), which were very close both ideologically and politically to Hitler's National Socialist German Workers' Party (NSDAP), rapidly gained

The rallies of Henlein's Sudeten German Party (SdP) were strikingly reminiscent of its model in the Reich.

influence among the German minority. Since their seditious activities were ever more visible, they were officially banned no later than 1933. Hitler's allies among the German minority were therefore forced to conceal their true political goals for some time. The Front of Sudeten German Homeland (SHF), headed by Konrad Henlein and renamed the Sudeten German Party (SdP) before the 1935 parliamentary election, became their haven. Its ideology and methods of political struggle it employed brought it ever closer to Hitler's own party.

The SdP achieved great success in the said parliamentary election with a full two thirds of the German voters in Czechoslovakia casting their votes for it, making it the second most powerful political party. That was in sharp contrast to the situation in previous years, when the majority of the German voters voted for German democratic parties, which had a respectable presence in the Czechoslovak government. Unfortunately, the trend continued thanks to the massive backing by Hitler's Germany as well as the terror and intimidation towards advocates of democracy among the German minority by Henlein's party members. As a result, the SdP received nearly 90% of the German votes in the 1938 municipal elections.

On the other hand, the democratic Czechoslovakia naturally became a refuge – or at least a frequent escape route – for thousands of German dissenters of the Nazi regime, persecuted for political or racial reasons. The German emigrants then arrived chiefly

Dr. Ludwig Czech was one of the German ministers in the inter-war Czechoslovak governments. He died as an inmate of the Terezín ghetto in 1942.

Numerous German emigrants found refuge in Czechoslovakia. Thomas and Heinrich Mann were granted Czechoslovak citizenship.

to Prague and the Czech borderland. They founded their organisations, published magazines and other propaganda materials, which were also distributed in Germany. Some, such as the world-renowned authors Thomas and Heinrich Mann, were even granted Czechoslovak citizenship. A number of Czechoslovak organisations, communities and individuals supported the German emigrants both morally and materially.

However, they were soon to lose this support, as Germany escalated its pressure on Czechoslovakia rapidly in the fatal year of 1938. In March, Hitler instructed Henlein during an appointment to continue raising his party's demands so that the Czechoslovak government could never meet them entirely. In May, Hitler signed a direction to prepare an assault on Czechoslovakia containing the sentence, "It is my unalterable decision to destroy Czechoslovakia by military action in near future."

The position of the Czechoslovak Republic was rapidly worsening. On the one hand, the borderlands were engulfed in a wave of terror aimed against German democrats and the Czech population; on the other hand, the allied Western powers – the United Kingdom and France – took the unfortunate path of 'appeasing' Germany, which factually opened a door for German aggression and made it possible for Germany to interfere more intensively with the internal affairs of Czechoslovakia. Lord Runciman's notorious mission went along similar lines: instead of striving to mediate an agreement between the Czechoslovak government and Henlein's party, he merely conveyed Hitler's demands to the Czechs.

The pressure of the Nazis and the Western Powers on Czechoslovakia

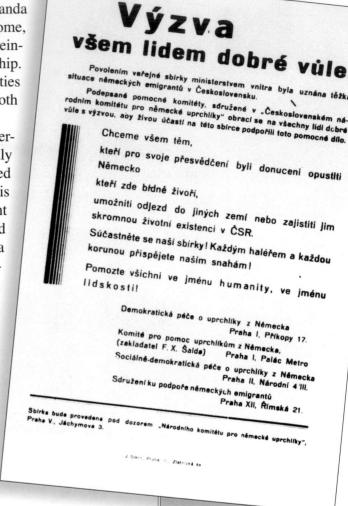

A fundraising call to aid German emigrants.

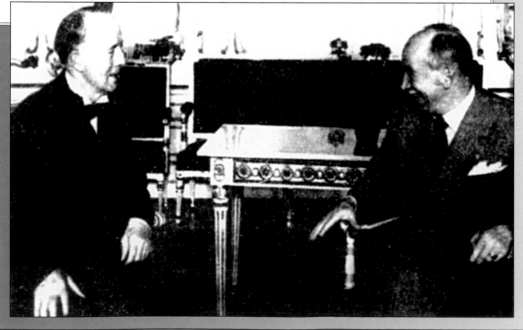

Lord Runciman, the British mediator in negotiations with Henlein's party, was the leading promoter of the 'appeasement' policy towards Hitler's Germany. He is pictured (left) visiting President Edvard Beneš.

culminated in September 1938. Following Hitler's seditious anti-Czechoslovak speech made at a Nazi Party congress in Nuremberg on 12 September, national authorities and certain groups of the population became targets of open assault in most borderland areas. In the latter half of September, SdP members were joined in the assaults by troops of the Sudeten German Freikorps, dispatched from Germany, where they had been trained and armed. The authorities did regain control over the borderlands, the SdP was banned and its leaders fled to Germany, but at the same time, the pressure of the Western powers resulted in the Munich Conference, held on September 29-30, 1938. Delegates of Germany, Italy, the United Kingdom and France decided, in the absence of Czechoslovak delegates, to sever the borderlands and pass them to Germany. The representatives of the participating powers presented the act as a rescue of European peace, but in fact it became an overture to the outbreak of a global war. Czechoslovakia was made Czecho-Slovakia for several months. After that, Slovakia first declared its independence in mid March 1939, and eventually the Czech Lands were occupied by Germany.

Arrests of Czechs and German opponents of Nazism broke out in the borderlands immediately after its annexation. The Jews were subjected to particularly severe persecution. Most of those who had not been imprisoned or killed in terrorist attacks fled. As a result, the Jewish population of the borderlands shrank to less than a tenth over a few months. The refugees headed for the Bohemian interior – Czechs, Jews, and Germans – passed through Terezín, which was now at the very edge of the curtailed country. Many of them were also quartered in Terezín temporarily for some time.

Armed Henleinists on a barricade near Cheb, September 1938.

The borderlands witnessed mass arrests of Czechs and German opponents to Nazism.

Food dispensation to refugees lodged temporarily in Terezín Small Fortress.

THE OCCUPATION OF CZECHOSLOVAKIA

L ess than six months after the unpropitious Munich Conference, the military units of the Nazi Germany occupied what remained of the curtailed territories of the Czech Lands on March 15, 1939. The garrison town of Terezín was among the first places to be occupied. In Prague on the following day, Adolf Hitler signed a decree establishing the Protectorate of Bohemia and Moravia, declaring the Czech Lands part of the Greater German Reich. The Protectorate was purely formally an autonomous state with its own administration and central authorities. In reality, it was under absolute control of the occupying authorities and its population was subjected to an extensive repressive apparat.

Dr. Emil Hácha was the head of the Protectorate – so-called State President – alongside the Protectorate Goverment representing the autonomous executive power. Their powers were minimal right from the start. Four such Governments took turns before the war ended. They gradually became instruments for promotion of collaborationism with the occupiers. Emanuel Moravec, the Minister of Education and Popular Enlightenment, was the dominant personality of the Protectorate Government after 1942; he became a symbol of unreserved collaborationism with the Nazis and betrayal of Czech national interests.

However, the occupiers would not settle for consistent control over the work of the Protectorate authorities and set up a parallel system of German political, administrative, judicial and policing authorities, overseeing all areas of life in the Protectorate.

The Reich Protector was a direct agent of Adolf Hitler and plenipotentiary of the Reich Government in the Protectorate. Konstantin von Neurath was the first Protector, succeeded by Reinhard Heydrich and Kurt Daluege (both as Acting Reich Protectors), and finally Wilhelm Frick. Karl Hermann Frank grew to be the greatest figure of the German administration in the Protectorate. Notorious for his pathological hatred towards the Czech people, his political career started in Henlein's Sudeten German Party, whose members joined the NSDAP, when the borderlands were annexed by Germany. Frank enjoyed Hitler's trust as the chief expert on the situation in the Czech Lands. First he held the position of Secretary of State, then he was appointed the German State Minister for Bohemia and Moravia in August 1943. Simultaneously, he was in command of the SS and police units in the Protectorate. The factual power was thus concentrated in his hands, while the Reich Protector performed a more ceremonial function.

The decree establishing the Protectorate.

The Protectorate of Bohemia and Moravia was an artificial formation with a population of 7,456,000 and covering 48,901 square kilometres.

The ultimate goal of the Nazi policy in the Protectorate was the Germanisation of its entire territory. The greater part of the population was to be eliminated gradually; the rest, to be Germanised. The 1943 General Settlement Plan gave precise figures: out of the 7,485,000 Czechs, 3,625,000 were considered capable of Germanisation; in addition, 1,415,000 German settlers were to arrive in the Protectorate. The rivaling components of the Nazi apparat had differing ideas on the pace of this process. For the sake of maintaining peace in the Protectorate and above all, maintaining the full output of its economy, which was of great relevance to Germany's armament, it was decided to shift the main stages of the implementation of the above plan until the expected victorious end of the war, with only partial measures implemented during it. Those included steps towards the suppression of Czech culture (except entertainment genres), science and education. The occupiers methodically persecuted the Czech intelligentsia and restricted the Czech school system – taking the first opportunity to close down the Czech universities, abolishing numerous secondary schools and striving to Germanise the rest. At the same time, they used social demagogy in an attempt to win over certain strata of the Czech society – chiefly the working class employed in industries relevant to military production.

Minister of Education and Popular Enlightenment Emanuel Moravec delivering a speech.

K. H. Frank visiting German colonists in Košátky near Mladá Boleslav, September 1943.

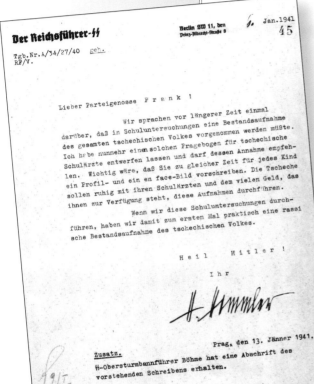

A letter from Reichsführer of the SS Heinrich Himmler to Secretary of State K. H. Frank in respect of questionnaires for the medical examination of Czech youth, utilised for a racial survey of the Czech population.

Even though the fates of those not to be Germanised were only to be sealed after the war, German settlers were arriving in the Protectorate already during the war and were settled in areas intended to form so-called German national bridges, meant to divide and gradually isolate areas with unbroken Czech populations. At the same time, an extensive racial survey of the Czech population was conducted under the guise of medical examination of Czech youth; its results were intended for a more accurate identification of those suitable for Germanisation.

The Germanisation efforts also included the subjugation of the Czech economy, manifested by the seizure of Czech banks and the related monetary diktat, introduction of a customs union, and the so-called Aryanization of Jewish possessions. The latter was grounded in the Reich Protector's Decree dated June 21, 1939 which made it possible to Aryanize, i.e., confiscate, even businesses with minimal Jewish ownership or "under Jewish influence". The degree of any such influence was decided solely by the German occupying authorities, and the Aryanized possessions were passed exclusively to Germans.

Out of the nearly 74,000 Protectorate Jews deported to the Terezín ghetto, less than 10,000 lived to see the end of the war in Terezín and various concentration camps. Leo Haas: A street in Terezín.

The Aryanization of the Jewish possessions was one of the steps towards their genocide. The said Reich Protector's Decree put the definition of Jewishness under the Nuremberg Laws of 1935 into force in the Protectorate. It constituted a pseudo-legislative basis for the adoption of many discriminatory regulations that separated Jews gradually from the majority of the population and deprived them of all possibility of leading normal lives. Towards the end of 1941, deportations of the Protectorate Jewish population began as part of the hideous design for a "Final Solution of the Jewish Question", envisaging the extermination of all European Jewry. Most of the Protectorate Jews were first transported to Terezín. The ghetto located in the town received some 74,000 people beginning on November 24, 1941. Czech Jews thus made up nearly one half of its coerced inhabitants.

The Protectorate Roma too faced a harsh fate: they were discriminated against and imprisoned in collection camps and coercion workrooms. The majority of the Roma were later deported to the "Gypsy Camp", part of the Auschwitz concentration camp complex. Only a few hundred of the original Roma population of the Czech Lands survived the Nazi genocide.

Reich Protector's Decree on Jewish possessions dated June 21, 1939.

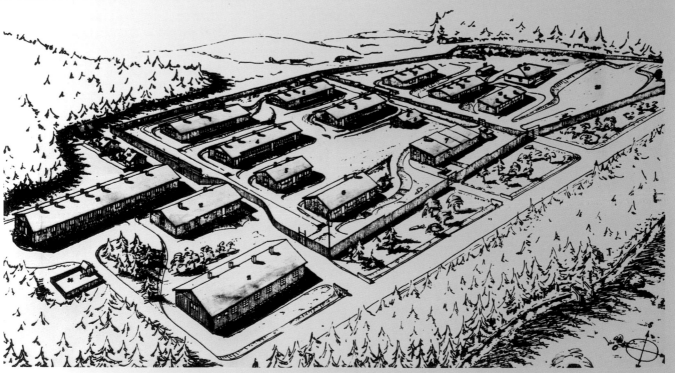

The gypsy camp in Hodonín near Kunštát was intended for Moravian Roma.

THE STRUGGLE OF THE CZECH NATION AGAINST THE OCCUPYING POWER

The struggle between the majority of the Czech population and the Nazi powers continued throughout the occupation. A number of resistance groups emerged over time. The Political Centre (PÚ) was formed by politicians and journalists soon after the Czech Lands were occupied; it strove for a restoration of pre-Munich Czechoslovakia. The core of the Petition Committee "We Remain Faithful" (PVVZ) was set up in the early summer of 1939 and involved a broad spectre of democratically oriented resistance activists. The Nation's Defence (ON) was the largest organisation within the democratic resistance movement in the first year of the occupation: it was set up by officers and soldiers of the former Czechoslovak Army. However, the Gestapo soon managed to penetrate its headquarters and struck hard against the entire structure in February 1940. The other resistance groups were also affected.

The Central Leadership of Home Resistance (ÚVOD) began forming in the early months of 1940 as the co-ordinating body of democratic resistance. Its goals, expressed in its agenda "For Freedom: Into a New Czechoslovak Republic", avowed the democratic ideals of the pre-Munich republic. Until 1942, the ÚVOD had a broad network of illegal resistance, but it suffered severe losses after Reinhard Heydrich was appointed the Acting Reich Protector and particularly during the reprisals following his attempted assassination. The network was rebuilt step by step in 1942-1944 and new resistance groups were formed. The setting up of the Preparatory Revolutionary National Committee (PRNV) was one of the results of those efforts.

Anti-occupation demonstration in Prague on October 28, 1939.

A Gestapo report on the Czech resistance movement.

- 2 -

Seit Juli 1941 hatte die UVOD wieder in Abständen von 2 - 4 Wochen Plenarsitzungen abgehalten, auf denen zum Teil auch General H o m o l a von der Militärorganisation teilnahm.

Am bemerkenswertesten an der Tätigkeit der UVOD ist das Unternehmen gewesen, erneut auf die Protektoratsregierung einzuwirken und ihr Weisungen der Londoner Regierung, die auf dem Kurzwellenfunkwege hierher gelangt waren, zu übermitteln. Zu diesem Zwecke hat sich ein von Dr. K o h a k beauftragter Redakteur Graf B o r e k - D o h a l s k y seit Juli 1941 je zweimal mit H a c h a und dem früheren Ministerpräsidenten E l i a š in Verbindung gesetzt und hat ihm Nachrichten der UVOD überbracht. Insoweit ist bereits gesondert berichtet worden.

Darüber hinaus hat die UVOD mit den Londoner Stellen wegen der Entsendung von tschechischen Fallschirmspringern zwecks Durchführung von Sabotagehandlungen verhandelt. Auf Anordnung Londons wurde im Protektorat ein günstiger Absprungplatz erkundet, dieser Platz und eine Anlaufadresse funktelegrafisch

24

[partial text, obscured] aussschuss der [...] den Fall der [...]ehen. Der Ab[...] Anfluges, wel[...]n wurde, durch [...]iumfeuer beleuch[...]ch bewaffnete [...]gesichert werden. [...] Zuge eines gegen [...]en erfolgten Luft[...]egend von Chrudim [...]tzt. Er konnte [...] Prag festgenommen [...]handelt es sich [...]er im Frühsommer

1940

2[...]

[partial text, obscured] ie csl.Le-[...]usammen-[...]and evaku-[...] ins Pro-[...]und Funk-[...]grosse Men-

[...]den letzten [...]der Zentral-[...]a m a n -[...]er ihm be-[...]er Organi-[...]ame D u b s -[...]f freiem

[...]lebenden [...]Reihen konn-[...]mmen wer-[...]keine Ver-

[...]t K r a j i n a .

[...]: (Nationaler Revolutionsausschuss)

[...]chgruppen konnte in den letzten Wochen, [...]er Festnahme des UVOD-Mitgliedes [...]m 20.10.41 sehr gut eingedrungen wer-[...]nnten namhafte Mitarbeiter des Natio-[...]nsausschusses, die sich bereits mit [...]en Arbeiten befassten, festgenommen [...]n diesen Personen lebten ebenfalls be-[...]unter falschen Papieren illegal. Be-[...]ise handelt es sich bei diesen Perso-[...]m Zuge der Prager Ermittlungen konnte [...]Fachgruppe, welche eine Unmenge von [...]l aus den letzten Jahren enthält, si-

chergestellt

Geheime Staatspolizei
Staatspolizeileitstelle Prag
- II BM -

Prag, den 10.November 1941.

Die tschechische Widerstandsbewegung

(Ergänzung zu dem Bericht vom 10.10.
1941)

Die Zerschlagung der tschechischen Widerstandsbewegung und der damit zusammenhängenden Nachrichtenapparate hat in den letzten 4 Wochen weitere Fortschritte gemacht. In dem nachfolgenden Bericht sind die wichtigsten Ergebnisse niedergelegt. Da im übrigen wiederum weitere enge Verbindungen der illegalen KPC zur Widerstandsbewegung festgestellt wurden, ist auch die Entwicklung auf diesem Gebiet kurz aufgezeigt worden.

I. Widerstandsbewegung.
1.) UVOD = Zentralleitung des heimischen Abwehrkampfes.

In den letzten vier Wochen konnte ermittelt werden, dass die Zusammensetzung der UVOD sich im Laufe des Herbstes 1941 dadurch verändert hatte, dass für festgenommene Angehörige andere Personen als Vertreter der Zivil-, Militär-bezw.Fachgruppe ernannt wurden. Für den festgenommenen Oberstleutnant B a l a b a n, der als Nachrichtenleiter des Zentralkommandos der Militärorganisation der UVOD angehörte, wurde der Organisationsoffizier des Zentralkommandos Oberst S r s t k a - Deckname D u b s k y - eingesetzt; für den festgenommenen Dr. H O L Y, der neben Professor K r a j i n a ein Vertreter der Zivilorganisation war, wurde in die UVOD der Redakteur Dr. K o h a k und für den festgenommenen Angehörigen der Fachgruppe A n d r s t ein Professor der Arbeiterakademie " H a v e l k a " ernannt.

Seit

Members of the Communist Party of Czechoslovakia (KSČ) went underground after the Party was abolished in December 1938. Most of the Party's leading officials left for Moscow, where they set up the KSČ leadership in exile. An illegal home leaderships controlled the work of the Protectorate communist groups. In consequence of repeated Gestapo strikes, four such leaderships were set up over time and the communist resistance activity was always resumed.

The home resistance received foreign aid chiefly through parachute units. Between 1941 and 1945, a total of 27 paratrooper landings in the Protectorate were made from the UK, where the Czechoslovak exile government was located. Paratroopers dispatched from the Soviet Union performed chiefly intelligence missions; they were also sent as organisers in 1944-1945. They were largely recruited among Soviet nationals experienced in guerrilla action. The activities of these paratroopers made a significant contribution to the mobilisation of the guerrilla (partisan) movement, which had been evolving in the Czech Lands from the latter half of 1942, and also registered in the growing influence of the communist segment of the resistance movement.

The occupying power faced manifestations of the Czechs' resistance with a massive repressive apparat, centred around the Gestapo with many territorial offices and headquarters in Prague and Brno.

The first mass manifestation of the Czech national resistance was the great demonstrations on October 28, 1939 – the anniversary of Czechoslovak independence. The occupiers struck back with hard persecution that took a heavy toll and was targeted primarily at students. Czech universities were closed down for three years, and in fact remained shut until the end of the war.

Both the intensity of the resistance movement and the numbers of sabotages in military production and transport increased after Germany invaded the Soviet Union. It was chiefly the sabotages that posed a threat to the operation of the military industry in the Protectorate. The fact that Reinhard Heydrich, the head of the entire repressive apparat in Nazi Germany, chief of the Reich Security Main Office (RSHA), was appointed the Acting Reich Protector on September 27, 1941, gives a measure of the gravity of the situation. He declared a state of emergency in parts of the Protectorate on the following day.

The activity of the resistance movement increased sharply after Hitler's Germany invaded the USSR. The picture shows a petrol depot in Náchod on fire.

In the spring of 1941, the Ministry of National Defence of the Czechoslovak exile government began training volunteers in Scotland to aid the home resistance as paratroopers.

Erlaß

des Reichsprotektors in Böhmen und Mähren über die Verhängung des zivilen Ausnahmezustandes vom 28. September 1941.

In den letzten Tagen haben unverantwortliche, im Solde der Feinde Europas stehende Elemente eine Anzahl von reichsfeindlichen Einzelhandlungen begangen. Durch eine damit verbundene Propaganda haben diese Elemente versucht, die Bevölkerung des Protektorats Böhmen und Mähren in Gegensatz zu den Interessen des Reiches zu bringen.

Von der Bevölkerung, die in ihrem Großteil die Schicksalsverbundenheit der europäischen Völker mit Deutschland als Realität anerkennt, erwarte ich, daß sie sich keinesfalls von diesen Reichsfeinden provozieren läßt. Notwendig ist, daß jeder Ruhe und Ordnung bewahrt und seiner gewohnten täglichen Arbeit nachgeht. Jedem ordnungsliebenden Menschen wird der Schutz der Behörden zugesichert.

I.

Zum Schutze der Interessen des Reiches und der Bevölkerung des Protektorats Böhmen und Mähren verhänge ich daher unter Bezugnahme auf die Verhängung des zivilen Ausnahmezustandes vom 27. September 1941 mit Wirkung vom 28. September 1941 — 12 Uhr — bis auf weiteres für die Oberlandratsbezirke Prag, Brünn, Mähr.-Ostrau, Olmütz, Königgrätz, Kladno den

zivilen Ausnahmezustand.

II.

(1) Alle Handlungen, die die öffentliche Ordnung und Sicherheit, das Wirtschaftsleben oder den Arbeitsfrieden stören, sowie der vorsätzliche unerlaubte Besitz von Schußwaffen oder Sprengstoff oder Munition, unterliegen dem Standrecht des zivilen Ausnahmezustandes.

(2) Hierunter fallen auch alle Zusammenrottungen, Gruppenbildungen, Versammlungen in geschlossenen Räumen und unter freiem Himmel, auf öffentlichen Straßen und Plätzen.

III.

Wer die Kenntnis von derartigen Handlungen oder Vorhaben nicht den zuständigen Behörden sofort mitteilt, unterliegt wie der Täter dem Standrecht des zivilen Ausnahmezustandes.

Der Reichsprotektor in Böhmen und Mähren

Mit der Führung der Geschäfte beauftragt

gez. Heydrich

SS-Obergruppenführer und General der Polizei.

Výnos

říšského protektora v Čechách a na Moravě o vyhlášení civilního výjimečného stavu ze dne 28. září 1941.

V minulých dnech se dopustili neodpovědní, ve službách nepřátel Evropy jsoucí jednotlivci některých činů, namířených proti Říši. Propagandou s tím spojenou pokusily se tyto živly dostati obyvatelstvo Protektorátu Čechy a Morava do rozporu se zájmy Říše.

Očekávám od obyvatelstva, které ve své většině uznává osudové společenství evropských národů s Německem jako skutečnost, že se nedá nikterak vyprovokovati těmito nepřáteli Říše. Je třeba, aby každý zachoval klid a pořádek a šel za svou obvyklou denní prací. Každému, kdo dbá pořádku, je zabezpečena ochrana úřadů.

I.

Na ochranu zájmů Říše a obyvatelstva Protektorátu Čechy a Morava vyhlašuji tudíž, s poukazem na vyhlášení civilního výjimečného stavu ze dne 27. září 1941 s účinností od 28. září 1941 — 12.00 hodin — až na další v okresích Oberlandrátů Praha, Brno, Moravská Ostrava, Olomouc, Hradec Králové, Kladno

civilní stav výjimečný.

II.

(1) Všechny činy, jimiž jsou porušovány veřejný pořádek a bezpečnost, hospodářský život nebo pracovní mír, jakož i záměrné a nedovolené chování střelných zbraní nebo třaskavin anebo střeliva, podléhají stannému právu civilního stavu výjimečného.

(2) To se týká také všeho srocování, shlukování, shromážďování v uzavřených místnostech a pod širým nebem, na veřejných ulicích a náměstích.

III.

Kdo se o takových činech nebo záměrech dověděl aniž je ihned oznámil příslušným úřadům, propadá právě tak jako pachatel stannému právu civilního stavu výjimečného.

Říšský protektor v Čechách a na Moravě

Pověřen vedením funkcí

pod. Heydrich

SS-Obergruppenführer a generál policie.

Reinhard Heydrich, appointed the Acting Reich Protector with the task to repress the growing resistance movement, proclaimed a state of emergency in parts of the Protectorate on September 28, 1941.

Several hundred people were executed during it. The state of emergency was reinstated after the Czechoslovak soldiers sent from Britain attempted his assassination on May 27, 1942; he died of the wounds a few days later. Courts-martial passed 1,412 death sentences during the martial law. The villages of Lidice and Ležáky were obliterated as part of the brutal retribution. The majority of their inhabitants were killed; others were deported to a concentration camp. The occupiers' terror did not even hesitate to kill the village children – the greater part were killed, while the rest were sent for re-education in German families.

K. H. Frank took over the occupiers' repressive policy after Heydrich's death. The basis of that policy was to set a tolerable degree of terror that would intimidate the national resistance into passivity yet not provoke a mass uprising. The policy sought to maintain a relative peace in the Protectorate and prevent strikes which would threaten the military production. Another objective was to discourage the population from supporting and collaborating with the guerrilla movement and to subvert the resistance groups.

One of the mass execution sites was in Luby near Klatovy.

The entire village of Lidice fell victim to the occupiers' reprisals following the assassination of R. Heydrich. It was burnt down on June 10, 1942, the men were shot and the women were deported to a concentration camp. The majority of the children were gassed, the rest were sent for re-education in German families.

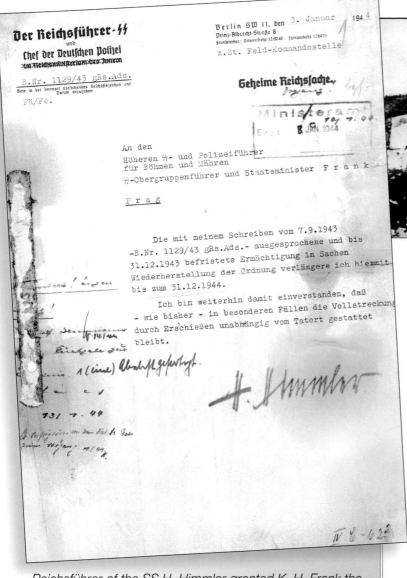

Special anti-guerrilla forces of the German security police took part in the terror against the Czech population from the autumn of 1944 onwards; they committed mass murders and burnt down villages. The picture shows the site of fire in Prlov.

Frank's powers encompassed the capacity to order executions without judicial proceedings, referred to as Sonderbehandlung (special treatment). Many were also conducted in the Gestapo prison in the Terezín Small Fortress. The numbers of public executions, intended primarily to intimidate the population, grew rapidly towards the end of the war. Villages were also burnt down and their inhabitants murdered for allegations of assisting guerrillas (villages of Ploština, Zákřov, Prlov, Javoříčko).

The Czech National Council (ČNR) emerged as the umbrella organisation of the entire Czech resistance movement towards the end of the war. It comprised members of both the democratic and communist movements. In May 1945, it was in political control of the uprising that swept through Prague and many other towns and cities of the Czech Lands.

Reichsführer of the SS H. Himmler granted K. H. Frank the authority to order executions without trial on his own request on September 7, 1943. Himmler's letter of January 3, 1944, extended its effect for the entire year 1944.

The Czech national resistance culminated in an uprising against the Nazi occupiers in May 1945. The picture shows one of the barricades in Prague.

TEREZÍN GESTAPO PRISON AND ITS INMATES

T he establishment of the Terezín Gestapo prison is directly related to the mass arrests among resistance groups active in the Protectorate of Bohemia and Moravia that started in the autumn of 1939. The existing prisons were filled to capacity, forcing the Gestapo to look for additional suitable places. The Small Fortress in Terezín was in the focus as it had been used as a military prison and penitentiary before the occupation. It had two major advantages to the German police: it was easy both to guard and to access.

The definitive resolution to set up the police prison was made in June 1940, when the Small Fortress was assumed by Prague Gestapo Headquarters. It received primarily persons arrested by the Gestapo in Bohemia, but later also inmates from Moravia and the severed borderlands.

The admission office of the Terezín Gestapo prison.

A view of the administrative
courtyard with offices.

Roll calls took place in the First Courtyard. The Courtyard administration office on the left in the foreground kept records of the internees' labour assignment.

SS-Hauptsturmführer Heinrich Jöckel was the commander of the Small Fortress prison throughout its existence. He was the main culprit of the brutal treatment of the inmates. His assigned wardens were equally brutal. The best-known ones include Jöckel's deputy Wilhelm Schmidt, assisted by Stefan Rojko, Anthon Malloth, Rudolf Burian, Herbert Mende, and Albin Storch. The few less cruel wardens, such as Theodor Hohaus and Josef Sternkopf, were mere exceptions. Some of the wardens' wives were on duty as wardens in the women's ward.

Waffen-SS troops were in charge of guarding the entire Small Fortress and escorted the prison transports and work squads. The First Company of the SS Böhmen-Mähren guard battalion, stationed in Brno, were first deployed in the Small Fortress in early November 1940. They were replaced by the Second Company in April 1942, who were transferred speedily under the SS Prague guard battalion as its Fourth Company. Each guard unit was composed of up to 110 men.

Prison commander SS-Hauptsturm-führer Heinrich Jöckel, nicknamed Pinďa (Shorty) by the inmates.

A group of wardens in front of the First Courtyard.

Warden Elisabeth Schmidt, the prison deputy commander's wife, pictured.

A wardens' family idyll, Small Fortress.

An SS guard company were in charge of guarding the Small Fortress and escorting the prisoners.

The wardens employed assistants recruited from among the inmates, to whom they delegated part of their own powers. In addition to office jobs, they were employed as so-called kapos (foremen). Many of them did this job to the benefit of the inmates, but some abused their position and bullied the inmates.

Organised resistance activities or individual manifestations of resistance against the German occupation were the most frequent causes of imprisonment. People assisting persecuted persons or violating anti-Semitic regulations were also punished. Men and women imprisoned for sabotage at work and flight from forced labour made up a large group of the inmates. A considerable number of people were imprisoned in the Small Fortress for having committed economic and criminal offences, particularly after a part of the Pankrác judicial ward was relocated to the Small Fortress from Prague towards the end of the war. For several months in the spring of 1944, the Fortress also held a transport of convicts from

A warden's uniform.

The Fourth Courtyard was built in 1943–1944. Over 3,000 prisoners languished there in the last days of the occupation.

Railway workers were involved in the resistance movement as part of the PVVZ.

ACHTUNG !
POZOR !

WER	KDO
WEITER GEHT	PŮJDE DÁLE
WIRD ERSCHOSSEN	BUDE ZASTŘELEN

A warning sign in front of the Small Fortress.

the Dachau concentration camp who were building a new camp in the nearby town of Litoměřice, to be the largest sub-camp of the Flossenbürg concentration camp on Czech territory.

As a rule, the Small Fortress was not the end of the journey; rather, it was an intermediate prison. Its inmates arrived from Gestapo offices and the Pankrác prison, and were forwarded to courts and prisons, penitentiaries and concentration camps in Germany.

Initially, only men were interned in the Small Fortress, for whom two of its courtyards were designated (The First and Second Courtyards, the latter being the workroom courtyard). The Women's Courtyard (Third Courtyard) was only established after the assassination of R. Heydrich in June 1942. The Fourth Courtyard was built in 1943-1944 due to the insufficient capacity. The numbers of inmates fluctuated over time, but were constantly growing. The average count was 150 prisoners in 1940; it was up to 600 in 1941, it grew sharply to 1,200 in 1942, and was around 2,000 people in 1943-1944. It peaked in the last days of the war, when there were some 5,500 inmates. In total, Gestapo offices handed some 27,000 men and 5,000 women over to Terezín prison.

High-ranking officers of the former Czechoslovak Army were interned in the Small Fortress. General Hugo Vojta pictured.

Members of the illegal Communist Party made up a large part of the Small Fortress internees. Communist resistance fighter Cyril Šumbera pictured.

Entire groups were arrested in preventive or retributive operations. Even the officials of the physical education organisation Sokol were deported to the Small Fortress. President of the Czech Sokol Organisation JUDr. Jan V. Keller pictured.

Members of both the democratic and communist resistance movements were among the very first prisoners. About one thousand members of military resistance, particularly the Nation's Defence (ON), passed through the gates of Terezín. Further hundreds belonged to the Political Centre (PÚ), the Petition Committee "We Remain Faithful" (PVVZ), and many smaller resistance groups. The stream of the arrested resistance fighters continued to grow until the end of the war, and members of numerous newly established resistance groups (Second Secret Light Division, National Union of Czech Patriots) arrived in Terezín.

The communist resistance movement was struck severely. Communists arrested preventively were interned in the Small Fortress as early as March 1939, even before the Gestapo prison was set up. Over time, members of all the four illegal KSČ leuderships, local resistance networks and various pro-communist groups ended up in Terezín.

The stream of prisoners arriving in Terezín was directly influenced by interventions of the occupying power, particularly preventive and retributive mass arrests. During the first state of emergency, the Fortress admitted members of the destroyed physical education organisation Sokol, who were later deported to Auschwitz. Following the assassination of Acting Reich Protector R. Heydrich and the subsequent proclamation of the second state of emergency, Gestapo concentrated the relatives and supporters of the assassinators in Terezín. Later on, 293 of then were murdered in the Mauthausen concentration camp. A group of 84 secondary school students from nearby Roudnice nad Labem were interned in the Small Fortress under a feeble pretence; thirteen of them would never see their homes again.

Solitary cells (right) and one of the mass cells (below) of the Fourth Courtyard.

Terezín prison held some 2,500 foreigners. A Belgian drawn by Josef Kylies.

A women's ward was set up in the Small Fortress in June 1942. Drawing by Ema Blažková.

Wide-ranging swoops also brought villagers from guerrilla-supporting regions to Terezín. Jews fared the worst of all in the Small Fortress; they were interned for resistance activity, violation of anti-Semitic regulations, or offences committed in the adjacent Terezín ghetto. The wardens tortured and killed them with particular brutality for their Jewishness. In early 1945, the Small Fortress even held Jewish escapees from evacuation transports from concentration camps.

In addition, about 2,500 foreign nationals were interned in the Small Fortress, particularly from the then Soviet Union, Poland, France and Germany, as well as several hundred Soviet and British prisoners of war.

Jehovah's Witnesses were deported to the Terezín Gestapo prison for their religion. This post-war picture shows Libuše Štecherová, interned in the Small Fortress and the Ravensbrück concentration camp.

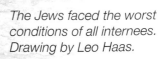

The Jews faced the worst conditions of all internees. Drawing by Leo Haas.

THE INMATES' EVERYDAY LIFE

The daily routines in the Terezín Small Fortress were dictated by the Prison Rules. Yet the inmates' living conditions worsened over time due to the general progress of the war, reprisals by German authorities against the Protectorate population, and above all, the inhumanity of the wardens.

An internee's stay in the Terezín prison started with an admission procedure in the Administrative Courtyard, lasting several hours. Over time, it incorporated torturing of the new arrivals by the wardens. Having been registered in the admission office, each prisoner had to hand in all their personal papers and valuables in the so-called Effects Room (Effektenkammer). The storeroom then issued a prisoner's outfit (typically an old uniform), a bowl, spoon and blanket. Only women were allowed to keep their civilian clothes. The admission procedure ended with an assignment of the new arrivals to their cells.

Morning and evening roll calls were part of the prisoners' lives.

Prisoner's clothes.

The numbers of prisoners in each cell were never stable. There were typically between 60 and 90 people in three-tier bunk beds. Apart from simple cabinets, the cell only contained a washbasin and a flush toilet. The situation was quite different in the newly built Fourth Courtyard, where several hundred inmates languished in each cell in absolutely unacceptable conditions.

Maintaining tidiness was a serious problem. Admittedly, a washroom was set up in the Small Fortress, but the inmates only had limited and irregular chances to use it. They were allowed to keep their underwear on arrival and to send it home for washing in certain periods, but they lost the latter opportunity towards the end of the war. Various parasites, particularly lice and fleas, soon became a terrible enemy. The setting up of the delousing facility in the First Court-yard brought little improvement. In spite of all their efforts, the inmates could therefore hardly maintain the cells tidy and themselves clean.

The quality of the prison diet was catastrophic. The prison management failed to observe even the low official standards and kept reducing the portions. By 1945, the daily ration of bread had gone down from the prescribed 370 grams to about half a pound per person per day. Besides bread, the inmates were only given a scoop of surrogate coffee twice a day and thin soup made from bad vegetables for dinner. Food parcels sent from home were the only bonus, but the wardens often plundered them or had them cooked into revolting concoctions dubbed Pinďablaf (Shorty's Filth). The inmates were thus constantly tormented by hunger, leading to dramatic decreases in body weight.

The prison cells were filled beyond hope at the end of the war, as recorded by a Fourth Courtyard Kapo (numbers of people in cells).

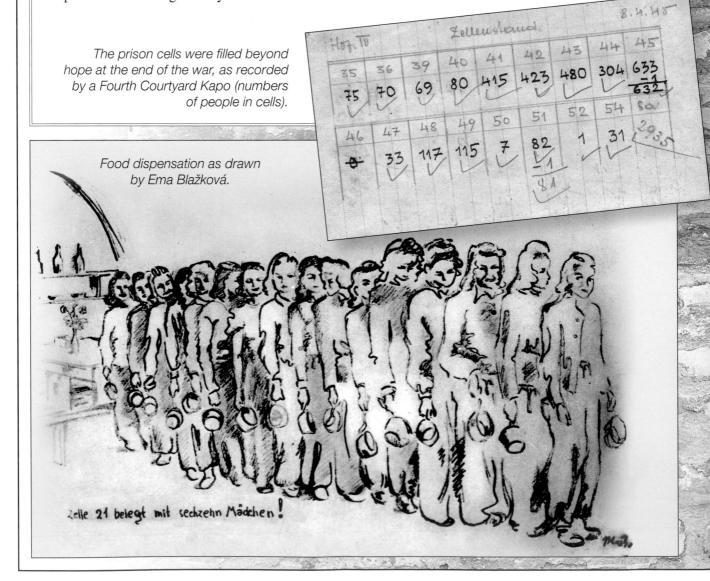

Food dispensation as drawn by Ema Blažková.

In these troubled conditions, the inmates sought solace chiefly in remembering their dearest ones and in mutual solidarity. Postcards were the only legitimate connection with the outside world; inmates were allowed to write a few lines of censored German text home. Their relatives sent them parcels of clothes, food and medicines. The inmates were also allowed to receive small sums of money to pay for barbers, postcards, drugs and soda. Visits directly in the prison were only allowed in exceptional cases. This lack of official contact led inmates to seek and use various ways of getting uncensored news from home. Secret messaging allowed them to send a lot of personal information as well as news of the investigation, which made it possible to warn fellows from the resistance groups who were still free. Civilians living near Terezín as well as civilian workers in businesses where the inmates were in forced labour helped to deliver many such messages. The latest news of the happenings in the Protectorate and at the fronts were heard from newcomers as well as via radio receivers in the electrotechnical workroom. Information exchange also existed between the women's and men's sections, be it in the sick bay, the laundry, the washroom or at work. However, such activities posed a great risk: wardens beat Josef Sládek dead for spreading the news from a foreign radio station in the spring of 1944.

Brief postcards in German were the only official connection with relatives.

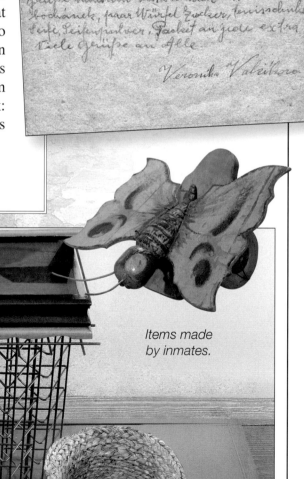

Items made by inmates.

The lack of contact with the outside world was partly overcome by the prisoners' mutual solidarity. The strict regime did not allow any significant social life, but at least the inmates had the evenings and Sundays to chat, remember their homes, families and work, play chess, draughts or cards. Some cells even held lectures on various topics ranging from science to the history of art, often of high professional quality. The priests of various churches also played an important role: they gave patriotic sermons, interpreted the Bible, and gave their cellmates spiritual support. The cell collective was cemented by celebrating Christmas, Easter and other holidays: above all the anniversary of the Czechoslovak Independence on October 28. That was even an opportunity for the inmates to organise various cultural programmes and sing in cells despite the strict ban on singing. Voskovec and Werich's songs and satirical lyrics on popular tunes were the favourites.

In addition, many excellent works of art originated in the Small Fort-

Josef Bernard's birthday card for his son.

Aloisie Páclová's illicit message on a foot insole.

Belief in God gave strength to many. Drawing by Běla Krausová.

ress. The composer Rudolf Karel even composed arias for an opera and other pieces. Both professional and amateur artists, such as Ema Blažková, Karel Štěch, Karel Štipl, Miloš Bič, and Josef Kylies, made hundreds of portraits of their cellmates and scenes from prison life. Many of the inmates even kept secret diaries, wrote poems, and made various little gifts.

Board games were played in free time.
Drawing by Karel Štěch.

Lectures on various topics crowned the social life in the cells. Drawing by Josef Kylies.

A cell discussion drawn by Miloš Bič.

Composer Rudolf Karel wrote his March of the Prisoners in Terezín.

Keepsakes made by inmates.

SICKNESS AND DEATH

Health and hygiene care was effected at a very low level in the Terezín prison compared to other similar facilities. Not even the police physician visiting the Small Fortress twice a week could oppose the management. The German physician Benno Krönert from Litoměřice was the longest-serving doctor in that position. However, Commander Jöckel seriously restricted his powers, and the ill were mostly treated as outpatients only. The infirmary was situated between First Courtyard cells 4 and 5.

Virtually all healthcare was thus provided by physicians among the inmates. Jan Konopík and František Vrátil's courage and selflessness contributed to the setting up of a sick bay as early as 1940, although it only had eight beds at first. The physicians were able to give their fellow prisoners basic treatment; however, they were limited by lack of common drugs and equipment. The medical care only improved in 1943, when the infirmary was fitted with instruments and devices confiscated from a Jewish doctor's surgery. The interned Poděbrady doctors Vojtěch Sailer, Václav Kryšpín, and Ladislav Filip also played a significant role; they succeeded in greatly extending the number of the sick bay beds to 74 in March 1944.

Most of the sick would not be admitted to the sick bay and had to stay in cells.
Josef Kylies: The sick around the stove.

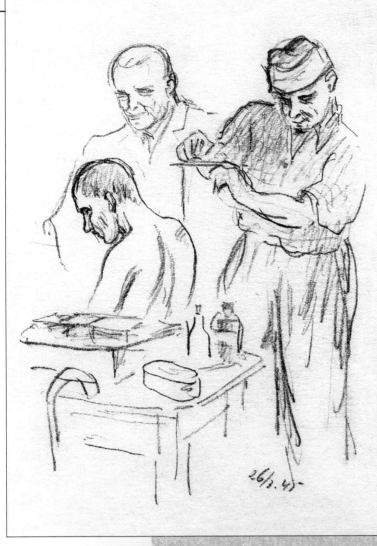

Josef Kylies:
Dr. Přemysl Poňka
doing surgery
with a razor blade
in cell no. 41.

Initially, medical care was provided in the First Courtyard only. The Women's Courtyard began filling in mid 1942; a physician from the men's sick bay attended to the women at first. A separate infirmary and sick bay was only set up in the Women's Courtyard after the first female physicians were interned.

Additional points of medical care were set up as the prison expanded. Infirmaries opened in the workroom courtyard and in the solitary block of the Fourth Courtyard over time. Numerous Czech physicians, such as František Nejezchleba, Karel Šrámek, Jaroslav Vápeník, Josef Souhrada, Přemysl Poňka, and the Pole Włodzimierz Oroński worked there. Even some of the collective cells of the Fourth Courtyard (nos. 35, 41, 45) were reserved for the sick in 1945, when infectious diseases spread.

In spite of lack of medical equipment and the primitive conditions, the prison physicians carried out numerous surgeries to save their fellows. The most remarkable ones included an appendectomy, a leg amputation, and a blood transfusion. Minor surgeries took place directly in the cells. It must be noted, however, that Jewish and Soviet inmates were denied even this modest medical care, so they had to rely on help of their Czech cellmates.

Josef Klouček:
Inmate
Dr. Jan Konopík.

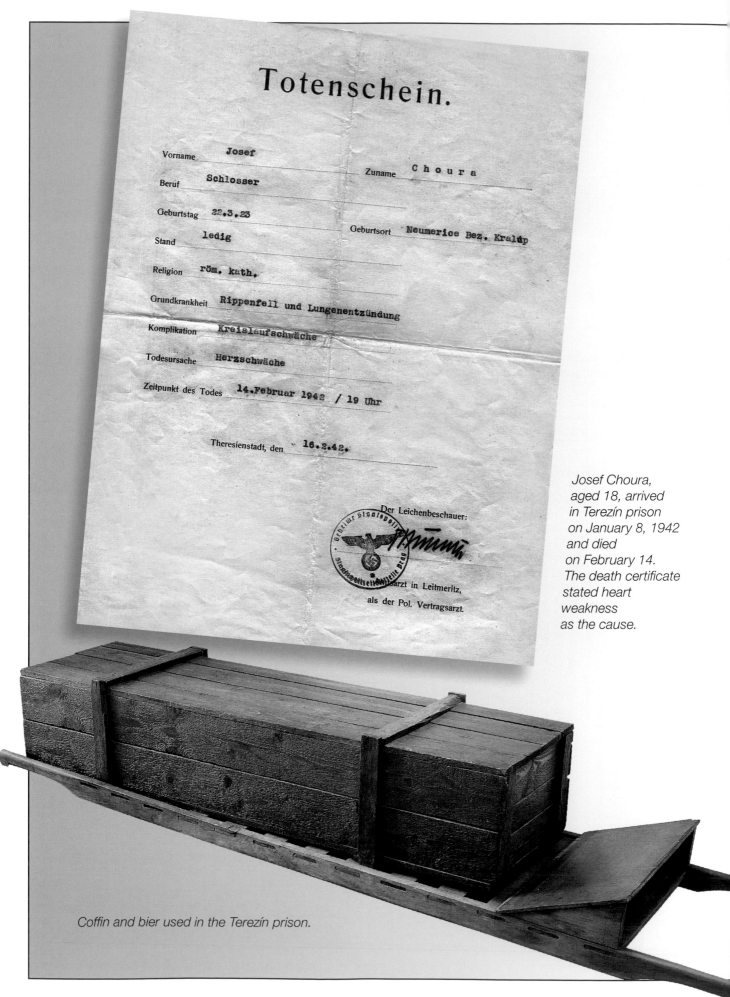

Totenschein.

Vorname	Josef	Zuname	C h o u r a
Beruf	Schlosser		
Geburtstag	22.3.23	Geburtsort	Neumerice Bez. Kralup
Stand	ledig		
Religion	röm. kath.		

Grundkrankheit   Rippenfell und Lungenentzündung

Komplikation   Kreislaufschwäche

Todesursache   Herzschwäche

Zeitpunkt des Todes   14.Februar 1942 / 19 Uhr

Theresienstadt, den   16.2.42.

Der Leichenbeschauer:

...arzt in Leitmeritz,
als der Pol. Vertragsarzt.

Josef Choura, aged 18, arrived in Terezín prison on January 8, 1942 and died on February 14. The death certificate stated heart weakness as the cause.

Coffin and bier used in the Terezín prison.

The lodging in large and overcrowded cells infested with parasites (lice, fleas), insufficient hygiene, bad meals, and frequent exhaustive labour enfeebled the prisoners both physically and psychically and resulted in impaired health. All that resulted in growing rates of disease and deaths.

A dysentery epidemic compelled the prison management to set up an infirmary in a building behind the First Courtyard in the autumn of 1944. Nevertheless, that still failed to compensate for the lack of real medical care. Logically, the worsening conditions in the prison resulted in a dramatically changing proportion of "natural" deaths to violent and induced ones.

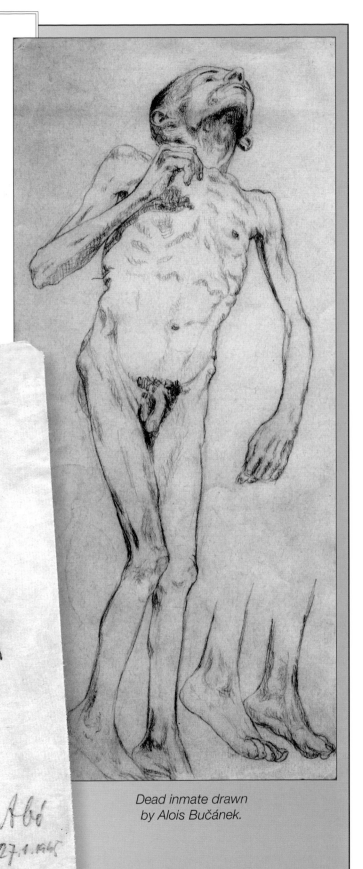

Dead inmate drawn by Alois Bučánek.

The inmates spent a lot of time fighting parasites. Antonín Bareš: Searching for lice.

Hanuš Taussig, member of the Leichenkommando, May 1945.

*Small Fortress mass graves were exhumed
between August 30 and September 4, 1945.*

Bubák funeral parlour did most of the funerals until October 1942. Afterwards, the dead were cremated in the facility built for the Terezín ghetto. The cremations ended in early March 1945 and from then on, the dead internees were buried in mass graves dug near the Small Fortress execution ground. A group of Jewish internees (so-called Leichenkommando) took the deceased, killed and executed to a morgue, located inside the bulwark behind the First Courtyard. Supervised by Head of the First Courtyard Stefan Roj-ko, the squad members undressed the corpses before taking them to the crematorium or a mass grave, and pulled out their gold teeth, which the SS-men took with them along with other former prisoners' valuables on their flight from Terezín in May 1945.

The unbearable living conditions, the cruelty of the wardens, and the executions brought the deaths of hundreds of internees in the Terezín prison in 1940-1945. Not one of the estimated 2,600 deaths can therefore be viewed as natural.

THE LABOUR ASSIGNMENT

Forced labour was part of the inmates' lives. A group of prisoners kept the related records in the First Courtyard Office. In 1940-1941, the inmates did various tasks inside the Small Fortress, primarily to secure the functioning of the prison. The number of the work groups grew along with the numbers of internees. Small groups worked directly in the prison administration and the effects store-room. Members of the supply squad, escorted by guards, accepted and sent mail, did the wardens' shopping and brought in the sodas. On their errands, they had the opportunity to contact people in nearby villages. Another group worked in the prison canteen, which included a potato store; this group became a haven for the elderly and sick thanks to the prisoners working in the First Courtyard Office.

Prisoners working in the timber store.

The supply squad (Karrkommando) in Bohušovice nad Ohří.

*Dozens of Jewish inmates were
tortured to death during the
construction of the fire water pool.*

The largest internal squad, the Baukommando, comprising up to 200 men in 1943, did various construction jobs inside the Small Fortress. Thomas Soukup headed it until 1944: he exposed the inmates at work to systematic torture. For example, the swimming pool was built chiefly by Jews and Roudnice students in 1942. The inhuman work pace, lack of tools, and Soukup's sadism cost many of the Jews their lives. The pool was intended as a fire water reservoir but doubled for the wardens' families' enjoyment. The Storchkommando, named after the warden Albin Storch, worked in the agriculture and landscaping around the Small Fortress. Assisted by kapos Hanuš, Lukič, Kukla and Grafik, Storch would torture his Jewish workers in many ways and beat them to death. Storch would often pick out an inmate and torture him for days until he died. It was no exception for the prisoners to bring in two or three dead bodies after work.

*Josef Kylies: Composer Vladimír Helfert
in the potato store.*

Prisoner workrooms for shoemaking, tailoring, smithy, locksmithing and electrotechnics, cabinetry and mechanical engineering were set up in 1941. They employed about 60 prisoners. The warden Josef Sternkopf was made their manager. He treated the inmates well and even tolerated their illegal activities. The cabinetry workroom made coffins, bunk beds, furniture for the SS canteen and offices, as well as various petty items for the wardens and Gestapo. There was even a prison printing works, fitted with equipment confiscated from the family of Jan Vojtíšek of Lázně Bělohrad, interned in the Small Fortress. It made postcards and forms for the prison administration. In 1944, about a hundred prisoners cut the hair off rabbit pelts in a wooden shack behind the former stables, dubbed the 'pelt house'.

A total of 42 internal squads worked in the Small Fortress in 1945. The working conditions varied, depending largely on the wardens' personalities. The Storchkommando and the Baukommando were among the worst: their employees were subjected to constant torture. On the other hand, the workrooms were among the least unbearable.

Women were not exploited for labour as much as men. They worked in the fields or tended the livestock. The seamstresses' workroom was the biggest women's squad, employing several dozen female inmates sewing and mending clothes, making bast insoles, and painting wooden buttons.

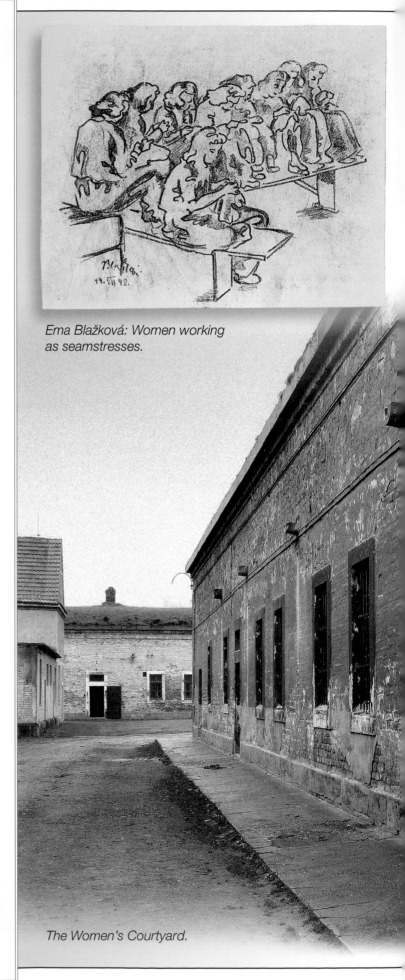

Ema Blažková: Women working as seamstresses.

Sorting potatoes on Trávčice farm.

The Women's Courtyard.

Inmates cleaning the wet moat in 1940.

The railway squad at Ústí nad Labem station.

Permanent exploitation of the workforce was not planned when the police prison was set up in the Small Fortress; only in 1941 did Prague Gestapo rule employment of Terezín inmates outside the Fortress. The external squads were sent to work in agriculture, industry and roadworks. The employers paid 55 pfennigs per hour of a prisoner's work. In connection with the external labour, the SS guard company was assigned a new duty of escorting and guarding the work squads.

At first, the prisoners would only go to work outside the Fortress occasionally, doing jobs arranged by the prison management with nearby businesses. In 1941-1942, some 30-40 prisoners were converting the cellars of the former Elbe Castle brewery in Litoměřice for military production. Beginning in 1944, Terezín prisoners worked along with German civilians in the new Albis-Werke plant, manufacturing military propellers. Nearly 300 prisoners worked in the Reichsbahn squad, upgrading the railway link and unloading the carriages. Additional groups worked in the Schicht factory in Ústí nad Labem, the Sputh factory in Lovosice, the Hněvice petrol storage facility, the Čížkovice cement works, and nearby brickworks. Over time, the total daily counts of workers learning for work exceeded one thousand. Prisoners dubbed

Anti-tank trench dug by prisoners between Terezín and Litoměřice.

the trench digging in the depression between Terezín and Litoměřice modern-day slavery. Over 1,000 men, including prisoners of war, worked there on March 16-28, 1945. The squad was supervised by young students of the Litoměřice SS college. They paid particular attention to the Jews: they shot 33 in only five days. The digging of an anti-tank trench was part of the fortification works done towards the end of the war where a Red Army strike was expected.

As part of the relocation of the military production underground, the construction of two underground factories commenced near Litoměřice in March 1944. The SS B5 Headquarters supervised the implementation of the project titled Richard. The workforce comprised chiefly prisoners of the nearby sub-camp of the Flossenbürg concentration camp, which interned over 18,000 people in 1944-1945. The death rate in the Litoměřice

Kommando	Su	35	36	40	41	42	43	45	48	49
Reichsbahn	300				1	14	284			
Schicht	40				40					
Schupo	50		23	25		8	2			
Birnau	8									
Wehrmacht	14	14			17					
Landrat	26	9			2					
Landrat Dr Illa	2									
Landratsamt	15	15								
4 Nachrschule KF2	26				26					
-"- I Lehrgr	12				12					
-"- Komdo	40	28			12					
-"- o stuf						50	250	6	224	80	40
Richard I	650				44					
-"- II	44				40	20				
-"- III	60						350			
-"- Nachtsch	350					2				
Grenzpolizai	2							11	39	
Sputh	50	8		22						
SS Hauptamt	50									

Counts of Fourth Courtyard prisoners working in external squads on April 9 - 16, 1945.

Work squads were headed by kapos, some of whom abused their office and tortured inmates alongside wardens and SS guards. A drawing by Bohumil Janda shows kapo Karel Spielmann, who took part in the murdering of Jews, in the foreground.

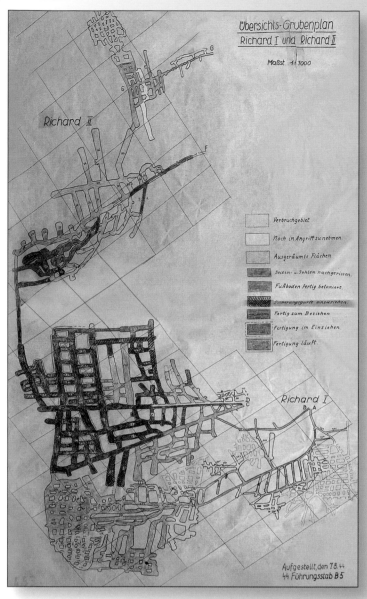

A plan of the Litoměřice limestone mine showing the status of works on the Richard project as of August 7, 1944.

camp was very high: about 4,500 people died due to epidemics, starvation and slave labour in less than a year. The factories were to be located in an exhausted limestone mine. The prisoners extended the underground caverns, cleared away the blasted limestone, and did bricklaying and other jobs. They built roads, a railway siding, a trans-shipment station, a water house, a gas line, offices and warehouses for contractors. Small Fortress inmates started work on the construction site in June 1944. The so-called Richard Squad, composed chiefly of Fourth Courtyard inmates, numbered 300 people at first and up to 1,100 eventually, working day and night shifts. The work on the Litoměřice site was among the hardest and most feared. Terezín inmates built the access road, did the clearing and bricklaying for Richard II (intended for Osram), and worked on the gas line construction. Workers in the Richard Squad and the trench-digging squad were decimated under the Nazi policy of destruction through labour (Vernichtung durch Arbeit).

Detached work squads were another type of prison labour; however, Terezín inmates were mostly deployed in small groups for one-time or short-term jobs. The Kladno squad was an exception: it existed in 1943-1944. Its members worked unloading railway carriages in the iron works, building the Gestapo offices, and doing the cleaning. Another detached squad was the group of prisoners working on the reconstruction of the Jenerálka Manor-house for Prague Gestapo in 1944-1945. In addition, twenty Jewish prisoners were employed digging trenches in a forest at Úpice near Trutnov in the summer of 1944. Another group of prisoners went to Nižbor near Křivoklát every year to prepare a Prague Gestapo holiday resort for the summer season.

The work squad in Úpice near Trutnov.

A showcase containing the drilling assembly found in the underground spaces of the Richard site near Litoměřice.

THE ESCAPES

Like in other Nazi repression facilities, escapes from the Terezín prison were attempted. In some cases the prisoners made the risky move believing they were scheduled for execution or destruction in a concentration camp. In other cases, they could no longer bear the appalling conditions in the Small Fortress and chose the risk associated with a break. However, the place was not made for escapes. The Small Fortress is surrounded with high bulwarks an escapee had to negotiate. Breaking off a work squad was equally difficult, as they were guarded by SS who were known to hesitate little before firing their guns.

Alois Kubíček's prison ID card,
stating 'Flüchtig' (escaped).

In spite of that, some of the inmates saw an escape as the only way to regain freedom. However, only few carried out their plans in face of the fear of possible persecution against their families and the physical difficulty involved. Several dozen prisoners attempted a break from the Small Fortress in 1940-1945; only few succeeded. The exact number of attempts is unknown. Fragmentary information about some of the escapes virtually comes only from the memories of former prisoners and their testimonials before extraordinary people's courts after the war. Detailed information is only available for escapes that ended dramatically in the Small Fortress.

For instance, inmate Binder, probably a technical college student, escaped using secretly made passkeys. He was caught and brutally beaten in the autumn of 1941. Another young inmate, František Soukup, got hold of gate keys and fled in the spring of 1942. Again, he was caught and beaten to death by Small Fortress wardens. The escape of an unknown Russian boy failed in 1943: he tried to hide on a lorry. Another Soviet prisoner succeeded in escaping off a train transferring the railway work squad from Ústí nad Labem in 1944. However, two Soviet prisoners were then shot exemplarily in the Fortress. Zdeněk Vlasta from the Elbe Castle work squad escaped in 1944, too, and was hiding at home until the end of the war. In the same year, Margit Ostringer was the only Reich German to escape from the Small Fortress; she was caught and returned.

Adolf Szinay-Szabó and Ladislav Malý made a tragic attempt to run from First Courtyard solitary cells on the night of July 10, 1944. Szinay was caught first, returned to the Small Fortress in September 1944 and beaten to death by wardens. Malý was caught too and executed in the Fortress on December 20, 1944.

Yugoslav Lieutenant Ivan Villágoš made another attempt, deserting from the Albis squad (airscrew manufacturing in Litoměřice). He was caught and tortured to death.

Josef Mattas, Miloš Ešner and František Maršík succeeded in escaping on December 6, 1944. They roped down into the wet moat through a gap in the bulwark, and managed to hide until the war ended.

Adolf Szinay-Szabó, beaten to death by wardens in September 1944 for attempting escape.

The attempted group escape from Fourth Courtyard cell no. 38 on March 3, 1945 had a tragic afterclap. Ladislav Šimek and Rudolf Vondrášek started, followed by Erwin Schmidt, who was shot and wounded on the cell roof and caught. He was then shot exemplarily alongside two other men and a woman in the tip of the Fourth Courtyard. Ladislav Šimek and Rudolf Vondrášek were both caught soon, tortured and beaten to death by Terezín wardens.

On April 19, 1945, Václav Štětka, member of the communist resistance, escaped from a work squad travelling to clear out air raid rubble in Lovosice. Supported by underground fellows, he lived to see the end of the war.

A

C

B

Prisoners who managed to escape together on December 6, 1944:
a) Miloš Ešner
b) František Maršík
c) Josef Mattas
*   (photographed in the 1980s)*

The yard by the First Courtyard solitary cells: the site of atrocious torture and beating to death, where wardens killed L. Šimek a R. Vondrášek, participants in the group escape from cell no. 38 of March 3, 1945.

An aerial view of the Small Fortress.

THE EXECUTIONS

T he Small Fortress shooting range became the site of executions of prisoners in 1943. Unlike under ordinary judicial proceedings, the arrestees were not given even a formal right to a proper trial and the executions were ordered solely by the Gestapo ("special treatment"). The firing squads were composed of the SS guard company, while some of the wardens volunteered.

Prison commander Heinrich Jöckel with the wardens.

The executions were by shooting: there was only one documented hanging of the prisoners. František Prokop, a communist resistance fighter, was probably the first victim of execution in the Small Fortress: he was shot on May 11, 1943. More executions followed in 1943, and their numbers grew in the following years.

František Prokop, the first executed prisoner in the Small Fortress.

The way to the execution ground: the so-called Gate of Death.

Executions took place at a shooting range in the moat.

Dr. Paul Eppstein, the former Elder of Jews of the Terezín ghetto, was shot in the Small Fortress on September 27, 1944.

The incurably ill were executed in the Small Fortress based on Himmler's decree 14f13. František Týc was maimed in cruel interrogation and shot on the June 10, 1944.

The killing of the incurably ill based on Himmler's decree 14f13 was a particularly atrocious crime, yet most of the executed were home resistance fighters, guerrillas and paratroopers. A mass execution of nine people put an end to the attempt of two Czech patriots to hijack an aeroplane to Slovakia in aid of the Slovak National Uprising in 1944. The public execution of three men and a woman in the

"Special treatment" also applied to paratroopers and guerrillas. Second Lieutenant Bohuslav Grabovský of the Intransitive descent was executed alongside other paratroopers in October 1944.

tip of the Fourth Courtyard on March 3, 1945 in retribution for several inmates' attempted escape was an extraordinary event. The foremen of all the cells were forced to watch the exemplary shooting. The last and biggest execution took place on the day Berlin fell: May 2, 1945. It took the lives of 49 men and three women, mostly members of left-wing underground groups (Předvoj, KSČ). An estimated 250 to 300 persons were executed in total in the Terezín Small Fortress.

An execution of nine put an end to the attempt of two Czech patriots to hijack an aeroplane to Slovakia. Věra Kuželová was executed alongside the others on November 4, 1944.

Milada Pixová, arrested for harbouring members of the illegal KSČ, was shot in the occiput by Jöckel's deputy W. Schmidt on October 9, 1944, as ordered by Prague Gestapo.

The last execution in the Small Fortress, May 2, 1945, drawn by former prisoner Karel Štěch.

INMATES' SUBSEQUENT LIFE STORIES

The Gestapo prison in the Terezín Small Fortress was an intermediate facility, where prisoners would not stay long as a rule. They were sent on to courts, prisons and penitentiaries or deported to concentration camps.

Nazi penitentiaries were designed for serving the sentences, while prisons were for custody. Most frequently, Terezín internees were deported to Dresden, Bautzen, Zwickau, Bayreuth, Waldheim, Berlin, Ebrach and Breslau (Wrocław). According to the incomplete information, over 4,200 men and women were sent before Nazi courts from the Small Fortress. Hundreds of them were sentenced to death and executed. The majority of the executions took place in 1944 and 1945. The growing numbers of the executions show how the harshness of the Nazi court sentences increased. While resistance workers were punished with confinement in the first period, the sentence was increasingly death in the latter years. Charges of treason and high treason were among the most serious misdeeds. Such cases were passed on by the German territorial courts in Prague and Brno to the People's Court of Justice in Berlin. Some cases were taken over by supreme territorial courts in Dresden or Breslau. Generally speaking, the court jurisdiction followed the division of the Protectorate: Berlin and Dresden courts dealt with cases in Bohemia; Breslau did Moravia. Minor cases were passed to German territorial courts in Prague and Brno.

An estimated 20,000 Czech nationals were imprisoned in Nazi prisons and penitentiaries; an uncertain number of them died of various diseases, during air raids in the last months of the war, and so forth. The prisoners deported from the Small Fortress made up about one fifth of those.

Terezín prison commander Heinrich Jöckel and the wardens' inhumanity and violation of prison rules stand out clearly compared to the conditions in other Nazi prisons and penitentiaries.

The Nazis employed the so-called protective custody in persecution of their opponents; the Gestapo inflicted it without judicial proceedings. The arrestees were then massed in concentration camps run by the SS. An extensive system of such camps grew in 1933-1945; the first Czech inmates arrived shortly after the occupation of the Czech Lands in 1939.

The introduction of the institute of protective custody and executions without judicial proceedings made the concentration camps institutions with unlimited power over the inmates' lives. The prisoners were exploited for labour in the German military industry and the price of one's life consisted in one's ability to work. The labour force was exploited regardless of the human losses.

Deportations to concentration camps greatly afflicted the Small Fortress inmates. Since the data are incomplete, the deportation of only 5,240 men and approximately 900 women can be proven reliably. Men were sent largely to the concentration camps at Buchenwald, Auschwitz, Flossenbürg, Mauthausen, Dachau, Sachsenhausen, and Gross-Rosen; women, chiefly to Ravensbrück. Hundreds of those would not stay in one camp: they would be moved on to other concentration camps and their sub-camps.

The majority of the 32,000 inmates of the Gestapo prison in the Small Fortress – 33 per cent – were deported to concentration camps; another 22 % were delivered to courts; 17 %, liberated in Terezín; 20 %, released; and 8 % died in Terezín.

Clothes and shoes of concentration camp prisoners.

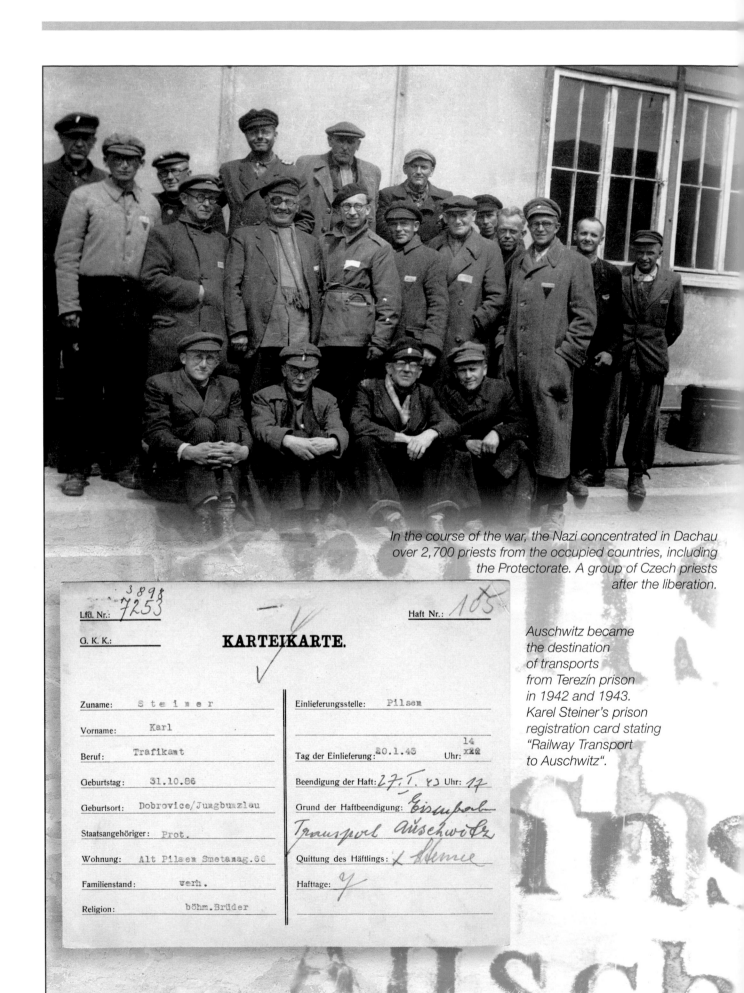

In the course of the war, the Nazi concentrated in Dachau over 2,700 priests from the occupied countries, including the Protectorate. A group of Czech priests after the liberation.

Auschwitz became the destination of transports from Terezín prison in 1942 and 1943. Karel Steiner's prison registration card stating "Railway Transport to Auschwitz".

Lfd. Nr.: 7253   3898

G. K. K.: _____

Haft Nr.: 105

KARTEIKARTE.

Zuname: S t e i n e r

Vorname: Karl

Beruf: Trafikant

Geburtstag: 31.10.86

Geburtsort: Dobrovice/Jungbunzlau

Staatsangehöriger: Prot.

Wohnung: Alt Pilsen Smetamag.66

Familienstand: verh.

Religion: böhm.Brüder

Einlieferungsstelle: Pilsen

Tag der Einlieferung: 20.1.43   Uhr: 14 XXX

Beendigung der Haft: 27.I.43 Uhr: 17

Grund der Haftbeendigung: Eisenbahn
Transport Auschwitz

Quittung des Häftlings: X Steiner

Hafttage: 7

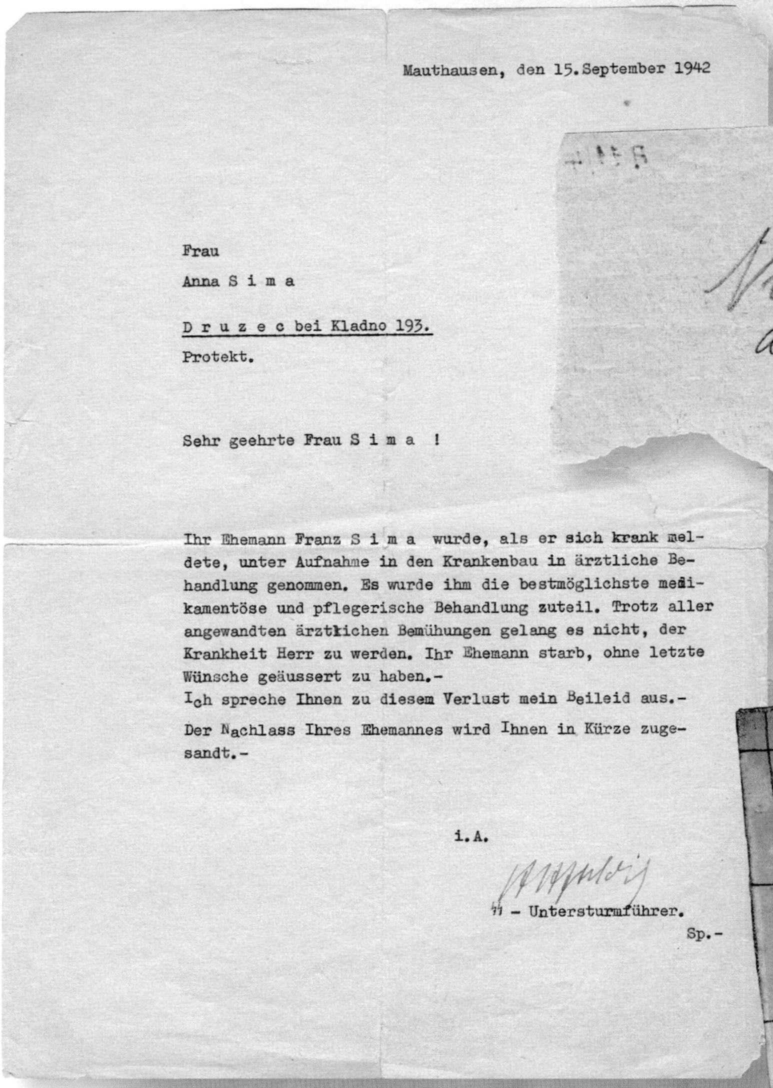

Mauthausen, den 15.September 1942

Frau
Anna S i m a

D r u z e c bei Kladno 193.
Protekt.

Sehr geehrte Frau S i m a !

Ihr Ehemann Franz S i m a wurde, als er sich krank mel-
dete, unter Aufnahme in den Krankenbau in ärztliche Behandlung genommen. Es wurde ihm die bestmöglichste medi-
kamentöse und pflegerische Behandlung zuteil. Trotz aller
angewandten ärztlichen Bemühungen gelang es nicht, der
Krankheit Herr zu werden. Ihr Ehemann starb, ohne letzte
Wünsche geäussert zu haben.-
Ich spreche Ihnen zu diesem Verlust mein Beileid aus.-
Der Nachlass Ihres Ehemannes wird Ihnen in Kürze zuge-
sandt.-

i.A.

SS - Untersturmführer.
Sp.-

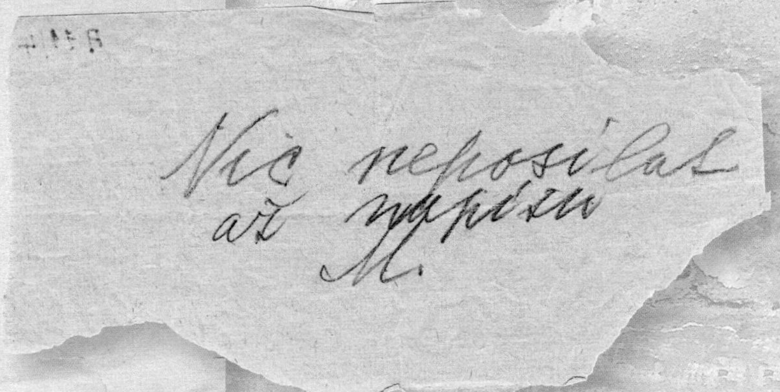

Marie Hornofová's last message to her family from Terezín. She would die after deportation to Auschwitz.

The cynical note sent to Anna Šimová, stating her husband's death in Mauthausen.

Anna Šimková embroidered a handkerchief with her various places of imprisonment.

Ravensbrück was the largest women's concentration camp, holding some 2,200 female Czech prisoners in 1939-1945, including several hundred deported directly from Terezín. An embroidery by Anna Kudrnová.

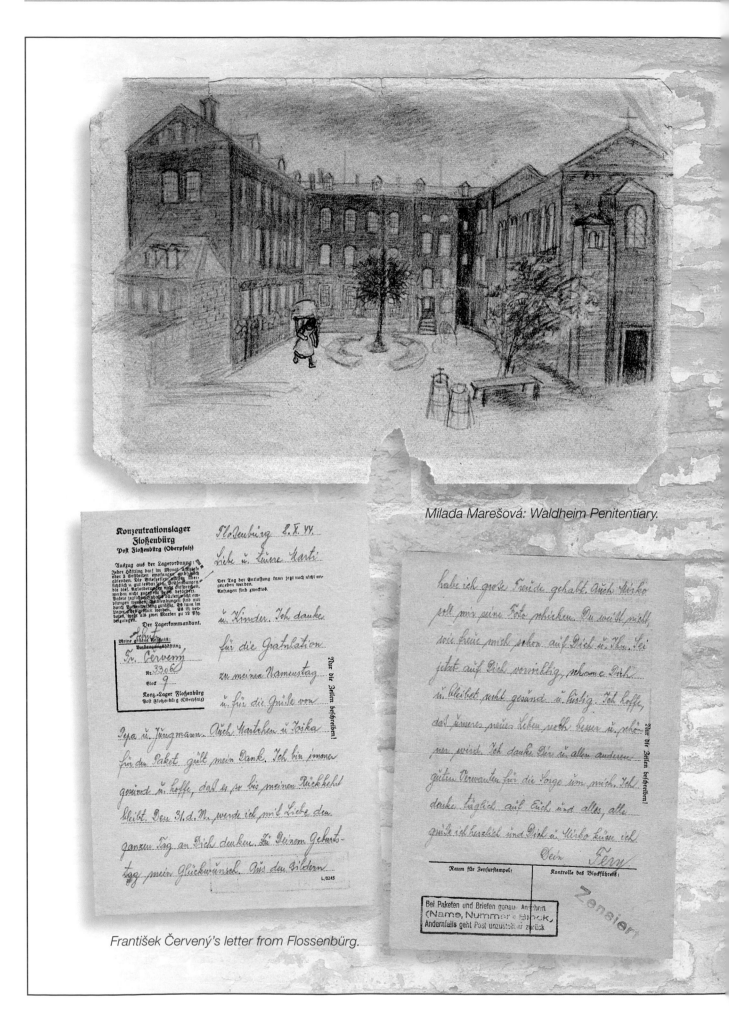

Milada Marešová: Waldheim Penitentiary.

František Červený's letter from Flossenbürg.

A portrait of the Czech inmate Jindřich Křesťan by an unknown cellmate.
Buchenwald, February 14, 1945.

THE YEAR 1945 AND LIBERATION

The war situation led to the end of deportations from the Small Fortress to other repression facilities in early 1945, causing the overcrowding of the cells and ensuing aggravation of the inmates' living conditions. The difficult conditions in the Small Fortress were further complicated in the last weeks of the war by an epidemic of spotted fever and typhoid, which contributed substantially to the high total death toll. A similar situation occurred in the adjacent Jewish ghetto, which received evacuation transports of prisoners infected with typhoid after April 20.

The health conditions in the Small Fortress motivated the Czech National Council in Prague – the supreme body of the Czech resistance movement – to launch an aid action for Terezín. Karel Raška, a Prague epidemiologist, was charged with its coordination. It started on May 2-3, 1945, assisted by Paul Dunant, a representative of the International Committee of the Red Cross who already had worked in the Terezín ghetto.

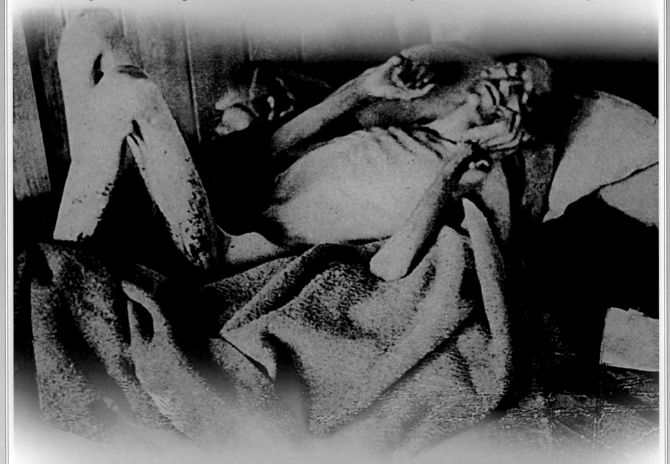

An ill and exhausted inmate.

In early May, the Terezín prison held some 5,500 inmates, of whom about 3,000 men were languishing in the overcrowded and lousy cells of the Fourth Courtyard, which was the most infested with dangerous infectious diseases. Its large cells contained hundreds of ill people, of whom many eventually fell prey to the typhoid epidemic.

The inmates languished most in overcrowded and lousy Fourth Courtyard cells in the last days of the war. Picture taken at Liberation.

Preparatory works for the aid action began both in Prague and around Terezín on May 4, 1945. The first group of medical and attendant staff of the Czech Action for Help (ČPA) arrived in Terezín on May 5, accompanied by 50 nurses, including students of the Prague Bulovka Medical College, who were going to graduate on May 30, 1945. A medical team from nearby Roudnice nad Labem and numerous other volunteers were involved in saving the prisoners.

When the Prague Uprising broke out on May 5, 1945, the prison staff and SS guards left Terezín. The prisoners and the ČPA people took control over the Small Fortress and began setting up makeshift infirmaries in the freed buildings. The ČPA personnel disinfected, deloused, bathed and examined the inmates. Warning signs and black and yellow banners fluttering over the fortress alerted the local Czech population to the danger of contagion.

The Small Fortress prison was dissolved by means of transferring the ill to auxiliary infirmaries that more set up by liberated Jewish inmates inside the former Terezín ghetto. Citizens and organisations in the broad surroundings of Terezín provided significant aid in the form of drugs, food and clothing. Some members of evacuation transports from concentration camps that had ended their distressful journeys in Terezín found a safe haven in the Small Fortress even after May 5, 1945. Thousands more arrived in the Terezín Jewish ghetto.

Inmates from evacuation transports resting in the Small Fortress.

The first Soviet tanks and combat vehicles passed through Terezín on May 8, 1945, on their way to aid Prague.

The forces of the First Ukrainian Group of the Red Army passed through Terezín in the early evening of May 8, 1945. A group of 53 Soviet military medics and numerous medical attendants with required equipment, including several field hospitals, delousing stations, etc., arrived in Terezín between May 11 and 13, 1945. The majority of the Soviet personnel stayed working in Terezín until July 9, 1945.

A strict fifteen-day quarantine was declared on May 14, 1945, and all of Terezín turned into a vast infection hospital. The deadly typhoid epidemic was only defeated in late May with substantial assistance of the Jewish physicians and nurses – former ghetto inmates working in the auxiliary infirmaries, where the ill from the Small Fortress were gradually shifted. The Czech

A group of Soviet military medics in Terezín.

Provisional hospital in the Women's Courtyard.

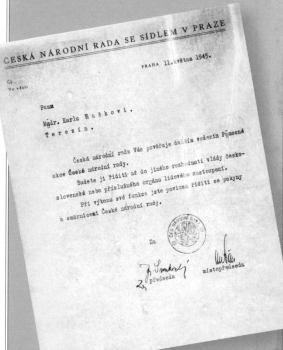

MUDr. Karel Raška, a Prague epidemiologist, was charged by the Czech National Council to lead the ČPA.

A showcase containing items used by the ČPA in Terezín in May 1945.

Action for Help (ČPA) members continued their selfless work.

After the quarantine was lifted, the former prisoners began repatriating: over 30,000 people moved until mid August 1945. The former prisoners spread to thirty countries of the world. The outstanding archievements of the aid action cost the lives of dozens of Czech, Jewish and Soviet doctors and nurses.

ČPA members disinfected and deloused the ill.

Victims of the typhoid epidemic.

THE EPILOGUE

The Allied Powers agreed already during World War Two to bring the war criminals before an international court of justice or deliver them for punishment in countries in which they committed their crimes. The investigation into the Nazi crimes included a review of the victims of Nazism.

The numbers of victims of the Nazi persecution in the Czech Lands were large. The German occupation brought loss of freedom to millions of Czechs, and death to tens of thousands. The extermination of Jews under the "Final Solution of the Jewish Question" took the most lives – no fewer than 73,000. In addition, approximately 6,000 Roma fell prey to racial persecution. Thousands more lost their lives in Nazi jails and concentration camps, where they were dragged after arrest. More were killed as a consequence of retribution against the home resistance and guerrilla movement and fell in armed conflict, chiefly during the Prague Uprising in May 1945.

The total balance includes 2,600 men and women tortured to death in the Gestapo prison in the Small Fortress, which played an important role in the Nazi repression system. In addition to that, the deaths of 1,685 men and 262 women deported from the Small Fortress to concentration camps have been documented. No fewer than an additional 255 men and women died after transfers to other prisons and penitentiaries. Of those who were delivered to courts from the Small Fortress, 453 men and 13 women were executed. However, the actual number of such victims was undoubtedly even higher.

General Bohuslav Ečer led the Czechoslovak delegation to the International Military Tribunal in Nuremberg; he participated in the international prosecution of war criminals.

On August 8, 1945, the Conference of the Four Powers in London resolved to establish an International Military Tribunal to try war crimes. The trial of the twenty-one major German war criminals took place in Nuremberg from November 14, 1945 to October 1, 1946. The Czechoslovak prosecution was represented by General Bohuslav Ečer, who had merit in the delivery of many war criminals to Czechoslovak justice.

Extraordinary people's courts were established in Czechoslovakia to try war criminals and their helpers; they passed hundreds of death sentences in the three post-war years.

The execution of the Small Fortress prison commander Heinrich Jöckel in Litoměřice.

Austrian authorities refused to deliver the warden Stefan Rojko to Czechoslovak justice. A territorial court in Graz condemned him to life imprisonment in 1963.

Many of the wrongdoers among the SS and their helpers (primarily some of the kapos) from the Small Fortress Gestapo prison were punished. The prison commander Heinrich Jöckel and his deputy Wilhelm Schmidt were executed upon sentences by the Litoměřice Extraordinary People's Court. Death penalties were also passed for the wardens Rudolf Burian and Albert Neubauer, and one of the firing squad commanders, Josef Lewinsky. The warden Thomas Soukup committed suicide in remand, as did Albin Storch in Dortmund in 1972. Another criminal, the commander of the First Courtyard Stefan Rojko, was condemned to life imprisonment by an Austrian court in 1963. A court in the former GDR condemned Kurt Wachholz to the death penalty in 1968. The wardens Anthon Malloth and Herbert Mende were sentenced to death in their absence, but both escaped their punishment. Malloth would live many years unpunished in Austria, Italy and Germany. Only in 2001 was he condemned to life imprisonment by a Munich court for the crimes he had committed in the Small Fortress. He died on October 31, 2002. On the contrary, Theodor Hohaus was exonerated for having helped the inmates.

Warden Kurt Wachholz being confronted with the former Small Fortress execution ground.

The Terezín prison deputy commander Wilhelm Schmidt after arrest.

The warden Anthon Malloth leading a contented life in a seniors' home near Munich.

The National Funeral of the exhumed victims of the Terezín prison, September 16, 1945.

The National Cemetery.

Mourning over the grave…

After the war, Terezín became a pilgrimage site for the Czech people. A National Cemetery was established in the Small Fortress foreground as part of the National Funeral held on September 16, 1945 in the presence of Minister of Foreign Affairs Jan Masaryk and former inmates Father Alois Tylínek, Dr. Milada Horáková and Ota Filip. The remains of inmates exhumed from the mass graves of the Small Fortress were interred during the funeral ceremony, laying the foundations of the National Cemetery, which would expand in the following years with the ashes of the victims of the last execution done in the Small Fortress on May 2, 1945, followed by more remains from Lovosice and Litoměřice. The remains of the casualties of the Terezín ghetto typhoid epidemic and of the victims of the Litoměřice concentration camp were also interred here. The first commemoration ceremony for the victims in Terezín took place on the anniversary of the Liberation in 1946; the Association for the Maintenance of the National Cemetery was established on that occasion. The Memorial to National Suffering then assumed care of the National Cemetery and was later renamed the Terezín Memorial.

TEREZÍN SMALL FORTRESS
1940-1945

A Guide to the Permanent Exhibition
in Terezín Small Fortress Museum

**Doc. PhDr. Vojtěch Blodig, CSc.,
Miroslava Langhamerová and Mgr. Jan Vajskebr**

The illustrations in the book
include materials from the Terezín Memorial collection
and documents and photographs from the National Archives
in Prague (6/1, 7/1, 8/1, 13/1, 15/1, 17/1-3, 21/1)
and Stanislav Motl's (77/5) and Dušan Tomášek's (9/3)
private collections.
Colour Photographs © Miloslav Hušek, 2009
Graphic Design: Ota Kaplan and Zdeněk Topolský
Translation © Petr Kurfürst, 2009
Responsible Editors: Markéta Stehlíková and Jindřich Kejř

Published for the Terezín Memorial
by Jitka Kejřová, V RÁJI Publishers (Prague 1, Tomášská 10)
as its 188th publication; 80 pages.
First edition, Prague, 2009, 2012
Printed by Východočeská tiskárna, s. r. o., Sezemice, 2012

ISBN 978-80-86758-64-0

www.pamatnik-terezin.cz